play guitar with...
chuck berry

Wise Publications
London/New York/Paris/Sydney/Copenhagen/Madrid

Exclusive Distributors:
Music Sales Limited
8-9 Frith Street,
London W1V 5TZ, England.
Music Sales Pty Limited
120 Rothschild Avenue,
Rosebery, NSW 2018, Australia.

Order No. AM943789
ISBN 0-7119-6536-6
This book © Copyright 1998
by Wise Publications

Compiled by Peter Evans
Music arranged by Arthur Dick
Music processed by Seton Music Graphics

Cover design by Pearce Marchbank
Computer layout by Ben May
Cover photographs from the Studio Twenty Archives

Printed in the United Kingdom by
Caligraving Limited, Thetford, Norfolk.

CD programmed by John Moores
Recorded by Passionhouse Music
All guitars by Arthur Dick

Your Guarantee of Quality
As publishers, we strive to produce
every book to the highest commercial standards.
The music has been freshly engraved and
the book has been carefully designed to minimise
awkward page turns and to make playing from
it a real pleasure.
Particular care has been given to specifying acid-free,
neutral-sized paper made from pulps which have not been
elemental chlorine bleached. This pulp is from farmed
sustainable forests and was produced with
special regard for the environment.
Throughout, the printing and binding have been planned
to ensure a sturdy, attractive publication which
should give years of enjoyment.
If your copy fails to meet our high standards,
please inform us and we will gladly replace it.

Visit the Internet Music Shop at
http://www.musicsales.co.uk

Music Sales' complete catalogue describes thousands
of titles and is available in full colour sections by subject,
direct from Music Sales Limited.
Please state your areas of interest and send a
cheque/postal order for £1.50 for postage to:
Music Sales Limited, Newmarket Road,
Bury St. Edmunds, Suffolk IP33 3YB.

guitar tablature explained

Guitar music can be notated three different ways: on a musical stave, in tablature, and in rhythm slashes

RHYTHM SLASHES are written above the stave. Strum chords in the rhythm indicated. Round noteheads indicate single notes.

THE MUSICAL STAVE shows pitches and rhythms and is divided by lines into bars. Pitches are named after the first seven letters of the alphabet.

TABLATURE graphically represents the guitar fingerboard. Each horizontal line represents a string, and each number represents a fret.

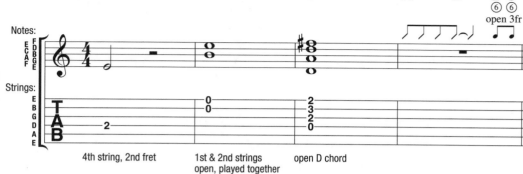

4th string, 2nd fret   1st & 2nd strings open, played together   open D chord

definitions for special guitar notation

SEMI-TONE BEND: Strike the note and bend up a semi-tone (1/2 step).

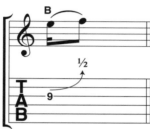

BEND & RELEASE: Strike the note and bend up as indicated, then release back to the original note.

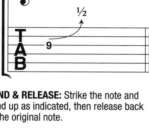

HAMMER-ON: Strike the first (lower) note with one finger, then sound the higher note (on the same string) with another finger by fretting it without picking.

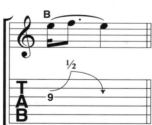

NATURAL HARMONIC: Strike the note while the fret-hand lightly touches the string directly over the fret indicated.

WHOLE-TONE BEND: Strike the note and bend up a whole-tone (whole step).

BEND & RESTRIKE: Strike the note and bend as indicated then restrike the string where the symbol occurs.

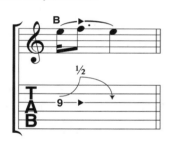

PULL-OFF: Place both fingers on the notes to be sounded, Strike the first note and without picking, pull the finger off to sound the second (lower) note.

PICK SCRAPE: The edge of the pick is rubbed down (or up) the string, producing a scratchy sound.

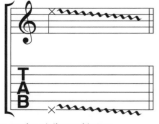

GRACE NOTE BEND: Strike the note and bend as indicated. Play the first note as quickly as possible.

PRE-BEND: Bend the note as indicated, then strike it.

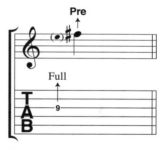

LEGATO SLIDE (GLISS): Strike the first note and then slide the same fret-hand finger up or down to the second note. The second note is not struck.

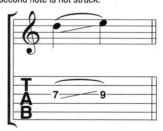

PALM MUTING: The note is partially muted by the pick hand lightly touching the string(s) just before the bridge.

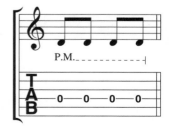

QUARTER-TONE BEND: Strike the note and bend up a 1/4 step.

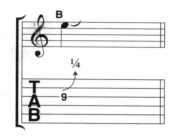

PRE-BEND & RELEASE: Bend the note as indicated. Strike it and release the note back to the original pitch.

SHIFT SLIDE (GLISS & RESTRIKE): Same as legato slide, except the second note is struck.

MUFFLED STRINGS: A percussive sound is produced by laying the fret hand across the string(s) without depressing, and striking them with the pick hand.

NOTE: The speed of any bend is indicated by the music notation and tempo.

around and around

Words & Music by Chuck Berry

sound,   well   you   ne - ver stop   rock - in',

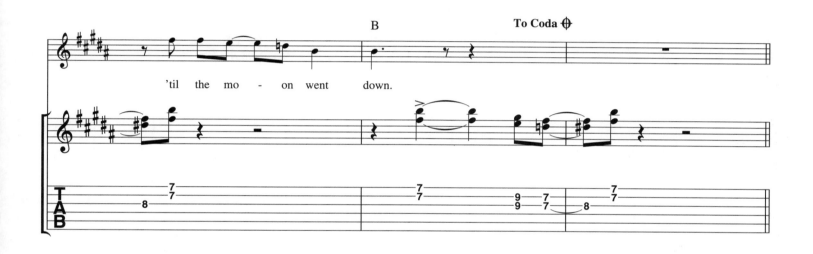

'til   the   mo - on went   down.

To Coda ⊕

Solo

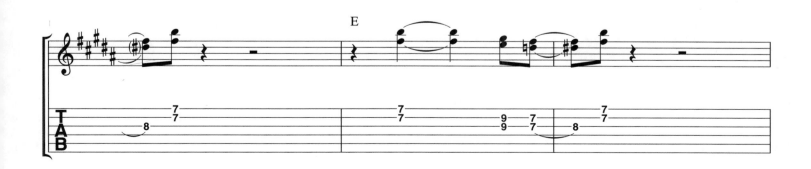

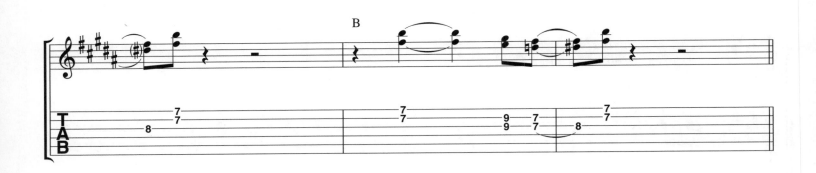

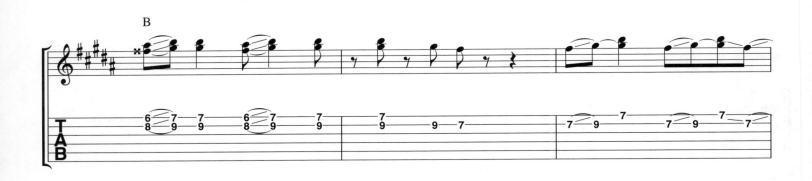

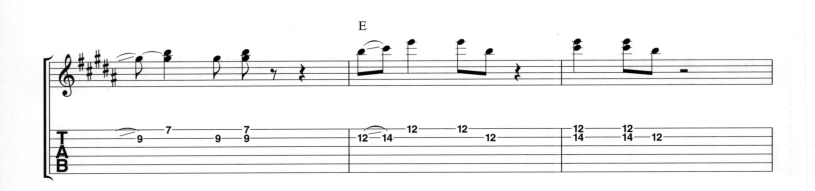

Well_____ they kept on a - rock - in',

go - in' round_____ and round,

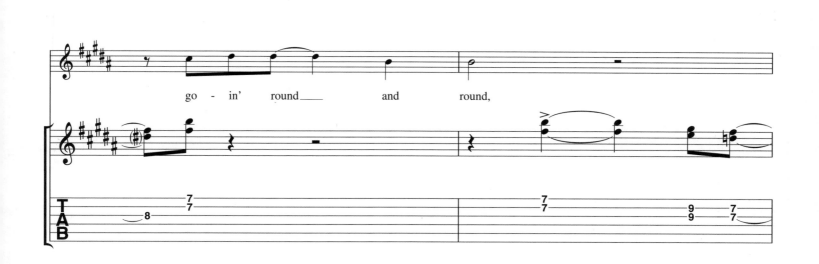

brown eyed handsome man

Words & Music by Chuck Berry

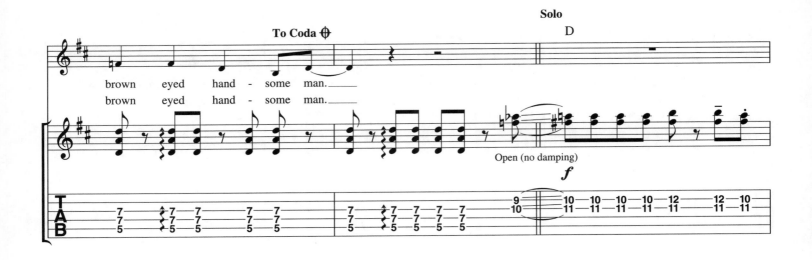

brown   eyed   hand - some   man.___
brown   eyed   hand - some   man.___

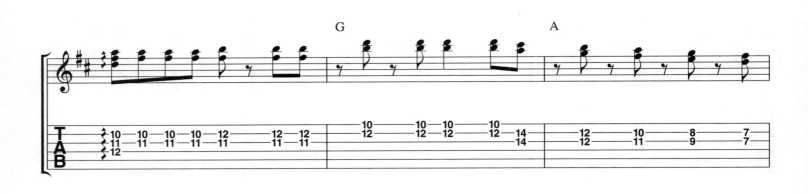

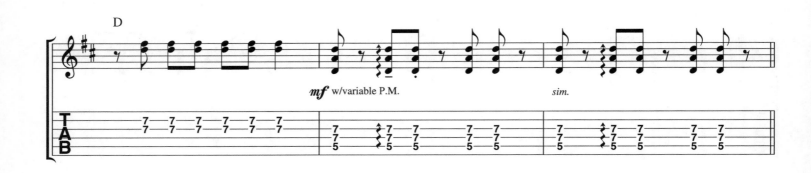

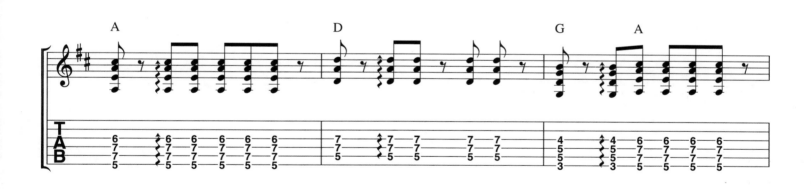

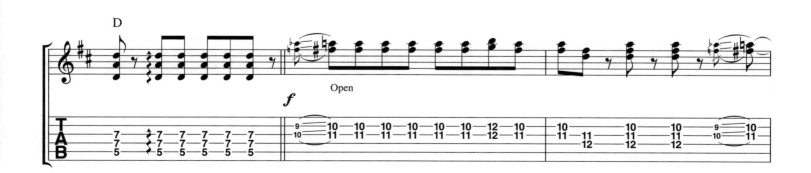

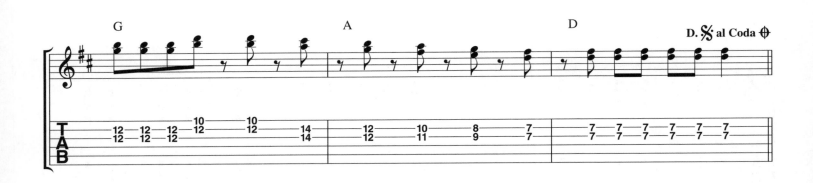

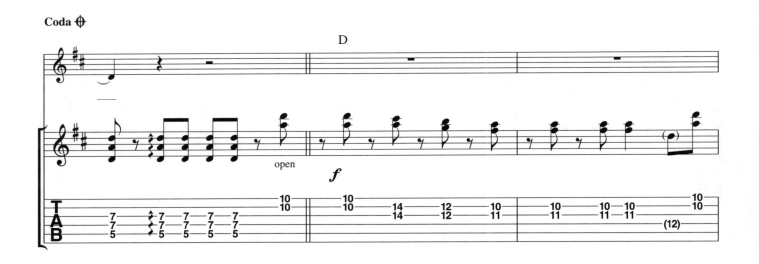

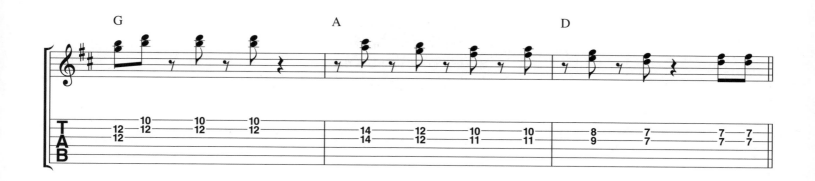

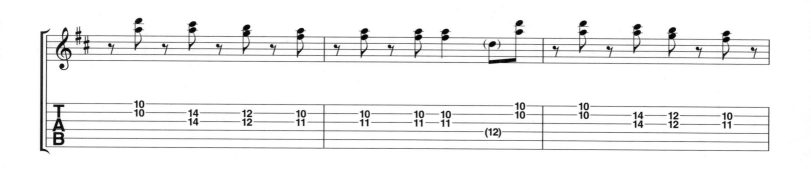

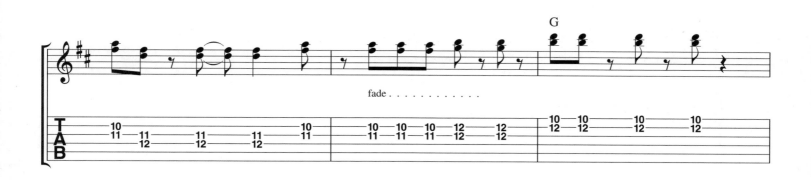

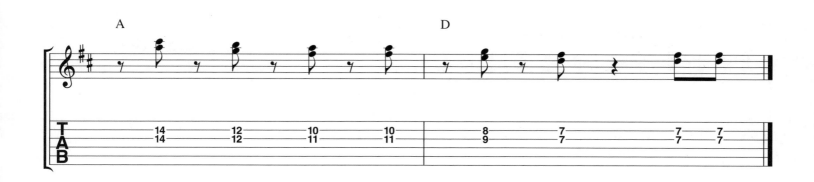

carol

Words & Music by Chuck Berry

- na learn to dance__ if it takes me all__ night__ and day.__

sim.

Verse

1. Climb in - to my ma - chine so we can cruise on__ out,__
wan - na hear some mu - sic like the boys are playin',

I know a swing - in' lit - tle joint where we can
hold tight,__ pat__ your foot, don't let 'em

jump and shout.__
carry it a - way.__
It's not too
Don't let the

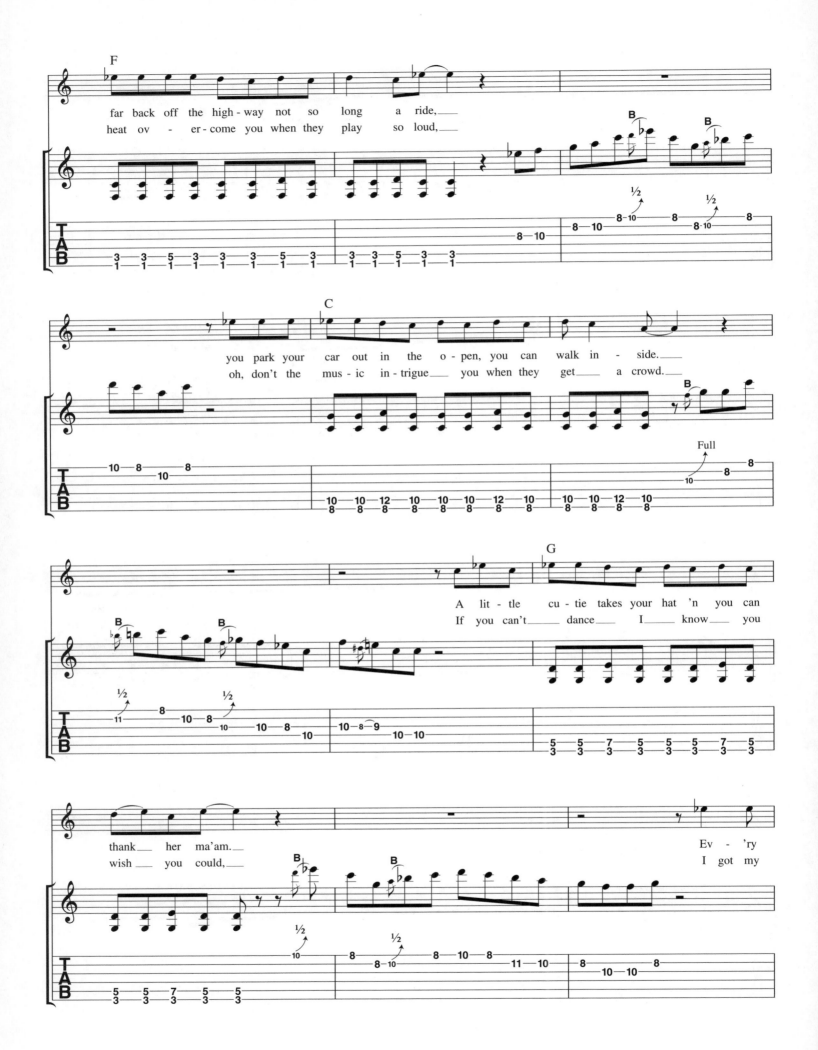

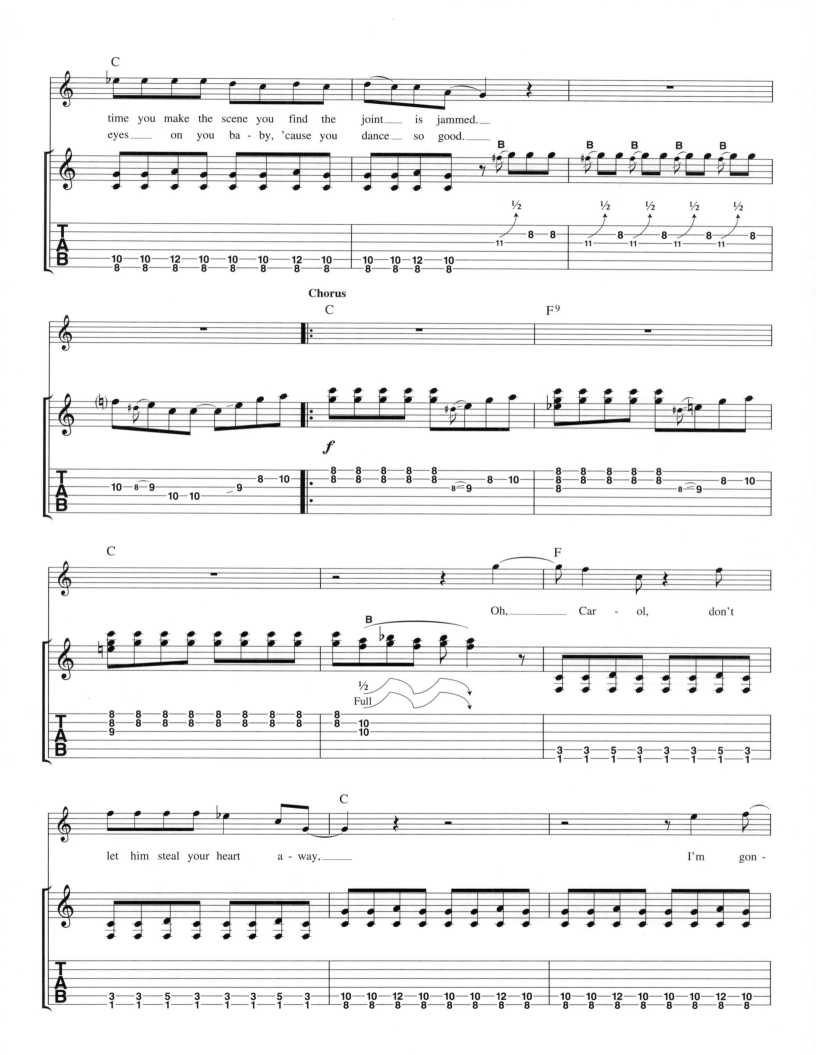

time you make the scene you find the joint____ is jammed.____
eyes____ on you ba - by, 'cause you dance____ so good.____

Chorus

Oh,____ Car - ol, don't let him steal your heart a - way,____ I'm gon -

- na   learn   to   dance   if   it   takes   me   all____   night   and   day.____

Repeat only on 𝄋

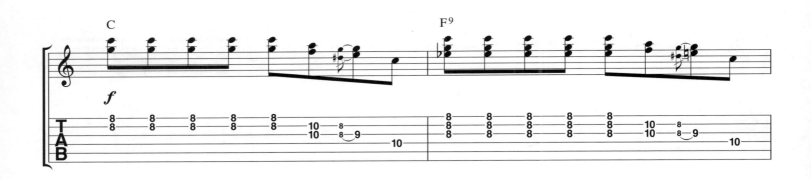

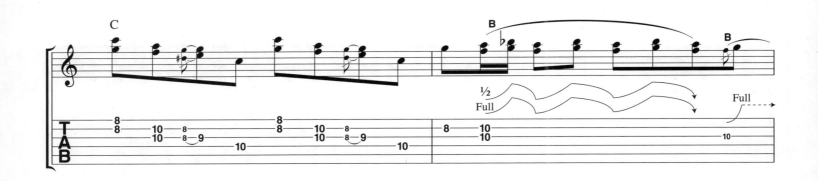

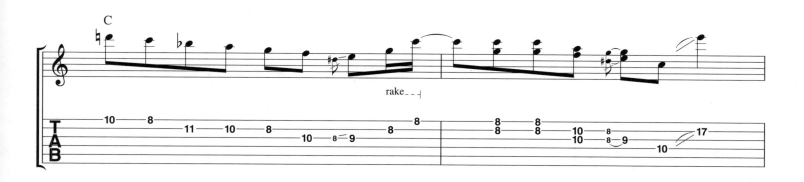

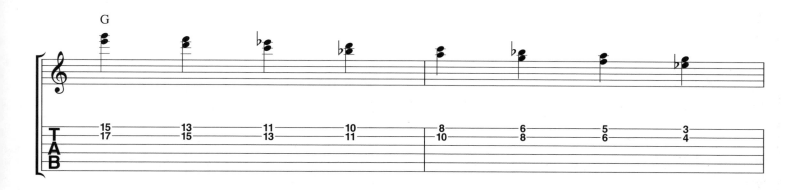

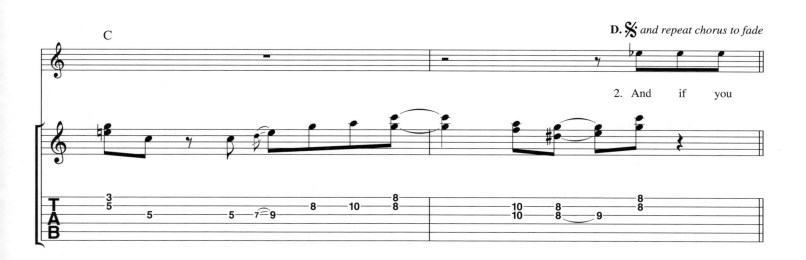

johnny b. goode

Words & Music by Chuck Berry

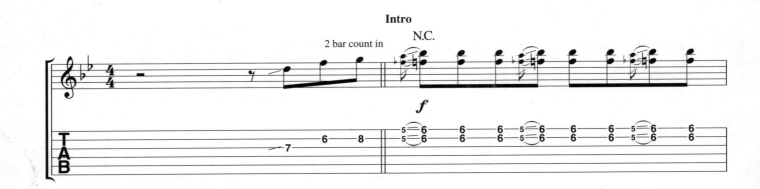

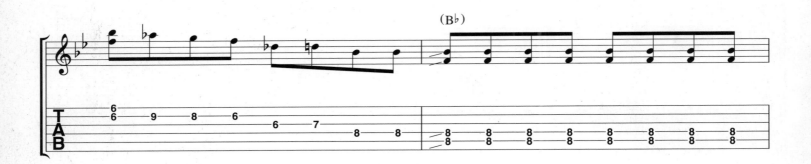

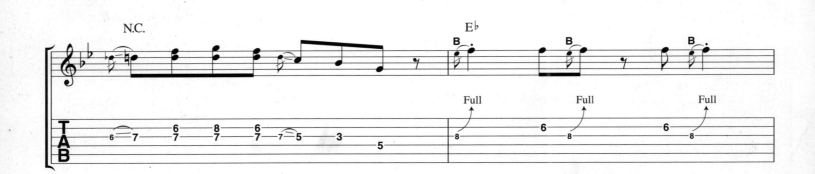

play *guitar with...*

the biggest names in rock

...**eric clapton,
jimi hendrix, john squire, kirk hammett,
mark knopfler, david gilmour, noel gallagher...**
and many more!

over 40 great titles

COMPACT
disc
MCPS

Made in the UK
©℗ Copyright 2000
Omnibus Records & Tapes

All rights of the record producer and the
owner of the works reproduced reserved.
Copying, public performances and
broadcasting of this recording prohibited.

play guitar with...

featuring...
**Authentic
transcriptions in
standard notation
and tab**

plus...
**Full band
performances on
the CD and separate
backing tracks for you
to play along with**

play guitar with...
all these

the music book...

- each book contains half a dozen classic songs presented in standard notation and easy-to-play tab, complete with chord symbols and lyrics.

the CD...

- hear the full-band performances on the accompanying CD (minus lyrics), then...
- take the lead and play along with the separate backing tracks.

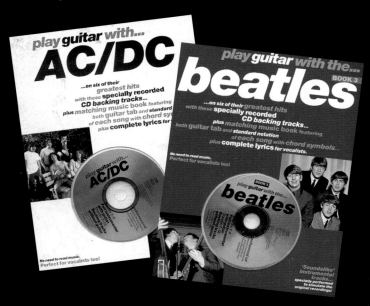

AC/DC
includes:
back in black
highway to hell
whole lotta rosie
Order No. AM955900

the beatles
includes:
day tripper
get back
yesterday
Order No. NO90665

the beatles book 2
includes:
eight days a week
please please me
ticket to ride
Order No. NO90667

the beatles book 3
includes:
here comes the sun
revolution
while my guitar gently weeps
Order No. NO90689

chuck berry
includes:
around and around
johnny b. goode
no particular place to go
Order No. AM943789

black sabbath
includes:
iron man
paranoid
war pigs
Order No. AM955911

blur
includes:
country house
girls and boys
parklife
Order No. AM935320

bon jovi
includes:
livin' on a prayer
wanted dead or alive
you give love a bad name
Order No. AM92558

eric clapton
includes:
layla
sunshine of your love
tears in heaven
Order No. AM950862

phil collins
includes:
another day in paradise
don't lose my number
one more night
Order No. AM928147

the corrs
includes:
forgiven, not forgotten
so young
what can i do
Order No. AM960971

the cranberries
includes:
hollywood
ridiculous thoughts
zombie
Order No. AM941699

dire straits
includes:
money for nothing
romeo and juliet
sultans of swing
Order No. DG70735

david gilmour
includes:
learning to fly
on the turning away
take it back
Order No.AM954602

buddy holly
includes:
rave on
words of love
peggy sue
Order No. AM943734

john lee hooker
includes:
boom boom
the healer
i'm in the mood
Order No. AM951885

b.b. king
includes:
every day I have the blues
rock me baby
the thrill is gone
Order No. AM951874

the kinks
includes:
all day and all of the night
waterloo sunset
you really got me
Order No. AM951863

kula shaker
includes:
govinda
hey dude
hush
Order No. AM943767

john lennon
includes:
cold turkey
happy xmas (war is over)
woman
Order No. AM943756

top bands and artists

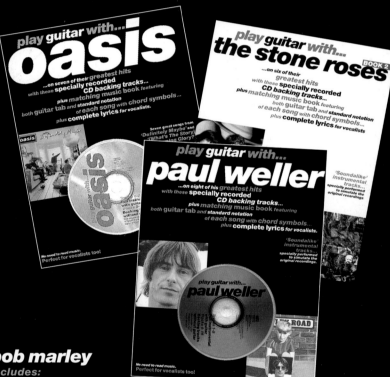

play guitar with... oasis
...on seven of their greatest hits with these **specially recorded CD backing tracks...** *plus* **matching music book** *featuring* both **guitar tab** and **standard notation** of each song with chord symbols... *plus* **complete lyrics** *for vocalists...*

Seven great songs from 'Definitely Maybe' and 'What's The Story? Morning Glory?'
No need to read music. Perfect for vocalists too!

play guitar with... the stone roses BOOK 2
...on six of their greatest hits with these **specially recorded CD backing tracks...** *plus* **matching music book** *featuring* both **guitar tab** and **standard notation** of each song with chord symbols... *plus* **complete lyrics** *for vocalists*

'Soundalike' instrumental tracks... specially performed to simulate the original recordings.

play guitar with... paul weller
...on eight of his greatest hits with these **specially recorded CD backing tracks...** *plus* **matching music book** *featuring* both **guitar tab** and **standard notation** of each song with chord symbols... *plus* **complete lyrics** *for vocalists*

'Soundalike' instrumental tracks... specially performed to simulate the original recordings.

No need to read music. Perfect for vocalists too!

play guitar with... the 70's
...on eight great hits from ac/dc, derek and the dominoes, dire straits, the eagles, free, slade, thin lizzy and wings with these **specially recorded CD ba...**
both **guitar tab** and st... of each song with chord sym... *plus* **complete lyrics** *for voca...*

'Soundalike' instrumental tracks... specially performed to simulate the original recordings

play guitar with... the 90's
...on seven great hits from eric clapton, manic street preachers, metallica, alanis morissette, oasis, pulp and the seahorses with these **specially recorded CD backing tracks...** *plus* **matching music book** *featuring* both **guitar tab** and **standard notation** of each song with chord symbols... *plus* **complete lyrics** *for vocalists*

'Soundalike' instrumental tracks... specially performed to simulate the original recordings

No need to read music. Perfect for vocalists too!

bob marley
includes:
i shot the sheriff
jamming
no woman, no cry
Order No. AM937739

metallica
includes:
enter sandman
fade to black
the unforgiven
Order No. AM92559

metallica book 2
includes:
creeping death
seek and destroy
whiskey in the jar
Order No. AM955977

alanis morissette
includes:
hand in my pocket
ironic
you oughta know
Order No. AM943723

oasis
includes:
cigarettes & alcohol
morning glory
supersonic
Order No. AM935330

ocean colour scene
includes:
the circle
the day we caught the train
the riverboat song
Order No. AM943712

elvis presley
includes:
all shook up
blue suede shoes
hound dog
Order No. AM937090

pulp
includes:
common people
disco 2000
sorted for e's & wizz
Order No. AM938124

the rolling stones
includes:
brown sugar
(i can't get no) satisfaction
jumpin' jack flash
Order No. AM90247

sting
includes:
*an englishman in
  new york*
fields of gold
*if you love somebody
  set them free*
Order No. AM928092

the stone roses
includes:
i am the resurrection
i wanna be adored
ten storey love song
Order No. AM943701

the stone roses book 2
includes:
fool's gold
love spreads
one love
Order No. AM955890

suede
includes:
animal nitrate
electricity
we are the pigs
Order No. AM955955

paul weller
includes:
the changingman
out of the sinking
wild wood
Order No. AM937827

the who
includes:
i can see for miles
pinball wizard
substitute
Order No. AM955867

the 60's
includes:
*all along the watchtower
  (jimi hendrix)*
*born to be wild
  (steppenwolf)*
*not fade away
  (the rolling stones)*
Order No. AM957748

the 70's
includes:
all right now (free)
*hotel california
  (the eagles)*
live and let die (wings)
Order No. AM957759

the 80's
includes:
*addicted to love
  (robert palmer)*
need you tonight (inxs)
*where the streets have
  no name (U2)*
Order No. AM957760

the 90's
includes:
*everything must go
  (manic street preachers)*
love is the law (the seahorses)
wonderwall (oasis)
Order No. AM957770

play guitar with...
sample the whole series with these special compilations...

the gold book
includes eight classic tracks:
jailhouse rock (elvis presley)
johnny b. goode (chuck berry)
layla (eric clapton)
sultans of swing (dire straits)
the healer (john lee hooker)
ticket to ride (the beatles)
woman (john lennon)
you really got me (the kinks)
Order No. AM951907

the platinum book
includes seven great songs:
a design for life
   (manic street preachers)
cigarettes & alcohol (oasis)
disco 2000 (pulp)
elephant stone (stone roses)
govinda (kula shaker)
the changingman (paul weller)
the riverboat song
   (ocean colour scene)
Order No. AM951918

Arthur Dick *has transcribed the music and provided the recorded guitar parts for most of the titles in the play guitar with... series, often bringing in other professional specialist musicians to achieve the most authentic sounds possible!*

A session guitarist with over twenty years' experience, he has worked with Cliff Richard, Barbara Dickson, Helen Shapiro, Bernie Flint and Chris Rea among others.

Arthur has played in many West End stage shows, and is in regular demand as a session player for TV, radio, and advertising productions.

He currently lectures on jazz and contemporary guitar at University Goldsmith's College, and works as a freelance production consultant.

Available from all good music retailers or, in case of difficulty, contact:

Music Sales Limited
**Newmarket Road,
Bury St. Edmunds,
Suffolk IP33 3YB.
telephone 01284 725725
fax 01284 702592**

www.musicsales.com

PUB04634

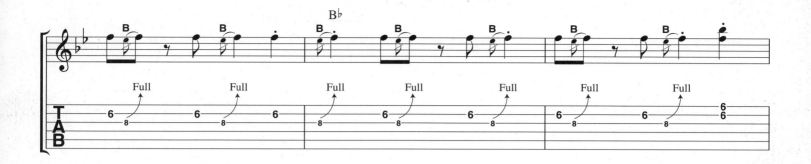

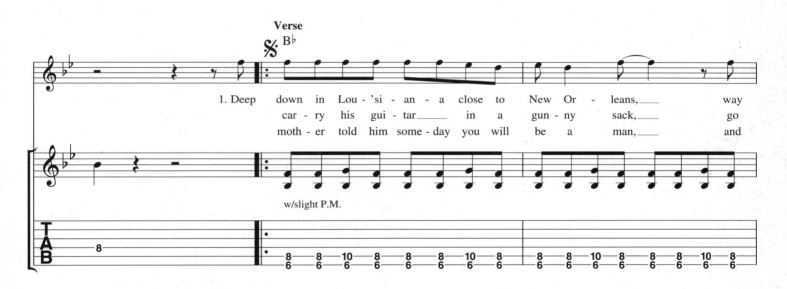

Verse

1. Deep down in Lou - 'si - an - a close to New Or - leans,_____ way
car - ry his gui - tar_____ in a gun - ny sack,_____ go
moth - er told him some - day you will be a man,_____ and

w/slight P.M.

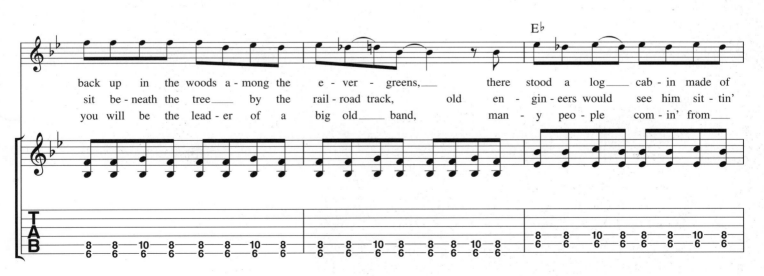

back up in the woods a - mong the e - ver - greens,_____ there stood a log_____ cab - in made of
sit be - neath the tree_____ by the rail - road track, old en - gin - eers would see him sit - tin'
you will be the lead - er of a big old_____ band, man - y peo - ple com - in' from_____

earth and wood,___ where lived a coun-try boy___ named Johnny B. Goode___ who
in the shade,___ strum-min' with the rhy-thm that the dri-vers made,___ the
miles a-round,___ to hear you play your mus-ic when the sun go down,___ may-

ne-ver e-ver learned to read or write so well,___ but he could play a gui-tar___ just like a
peo-ple pas-sin' by___ they would stop and say "Oh my,___ but that___ lit-tle coun-try
be some-day your name will be in lights say-in', "John-ny B. Goode___ to-night."

Chorus

ring-in' a bell.___ } Go! Go!___ Go,___ John-ny, go___ go!___
boy___ can play." }

ƒ 2° w/Rhythm Fig. 1

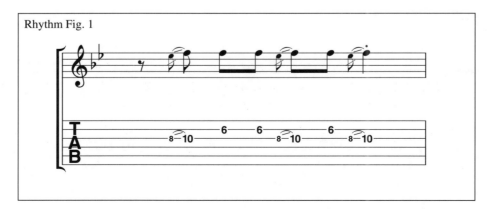

Rhythm Fig. 1

2. He used to

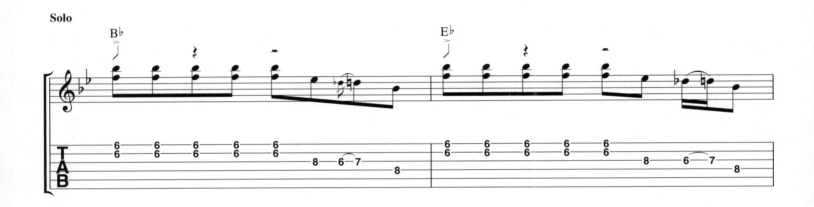

Solo

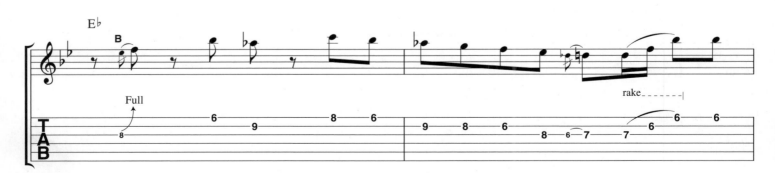

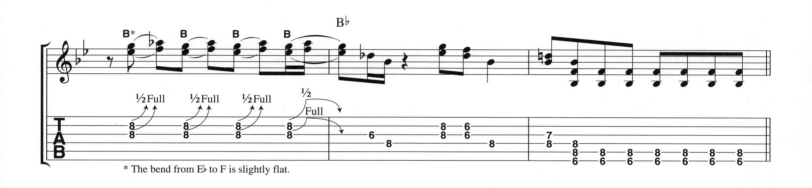

* The bend from E♭ to F is slightly flat.

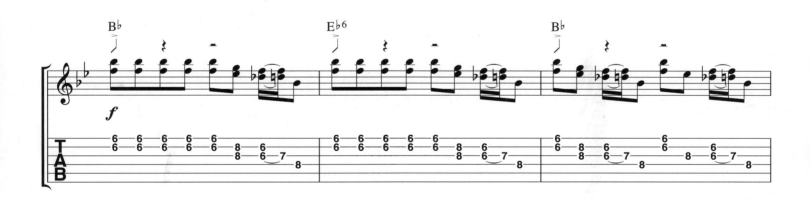

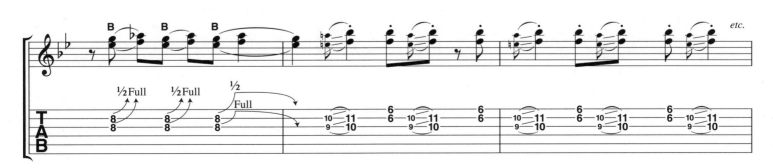

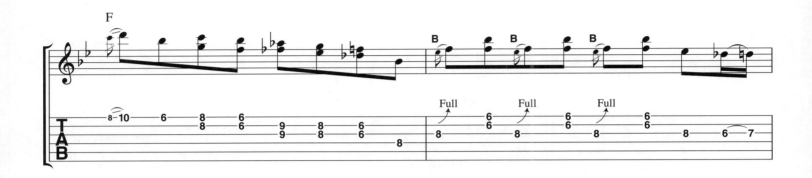

D. %. al Coda ⊕

3. His

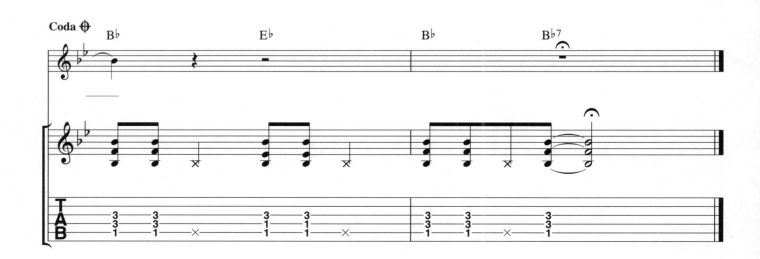

little queenie

Words & Music by Chuck Berry

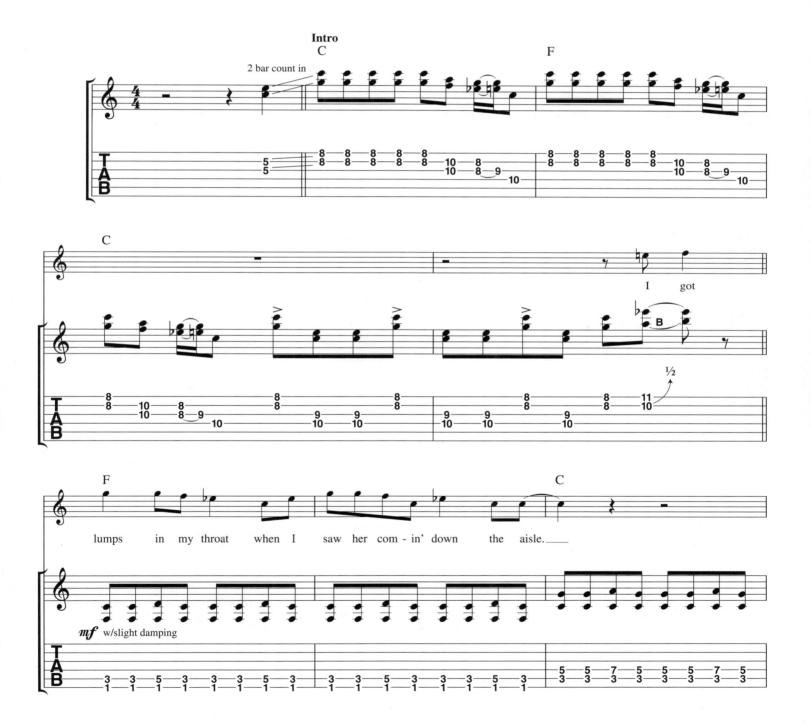

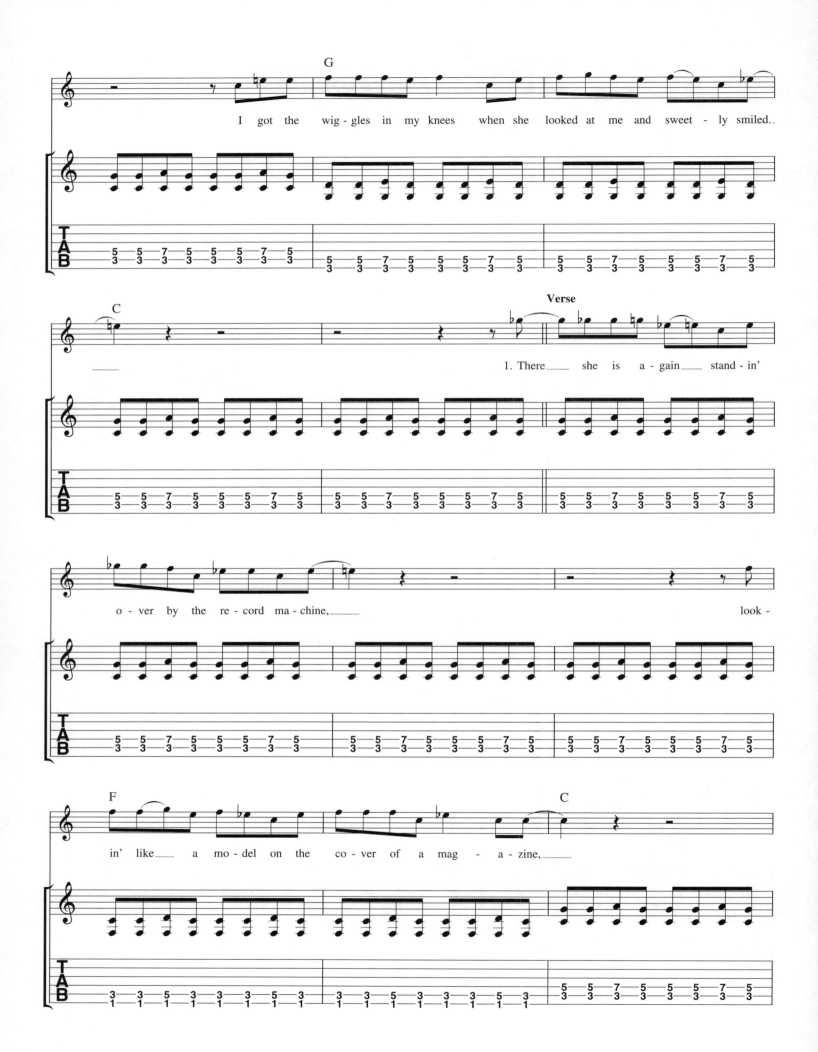

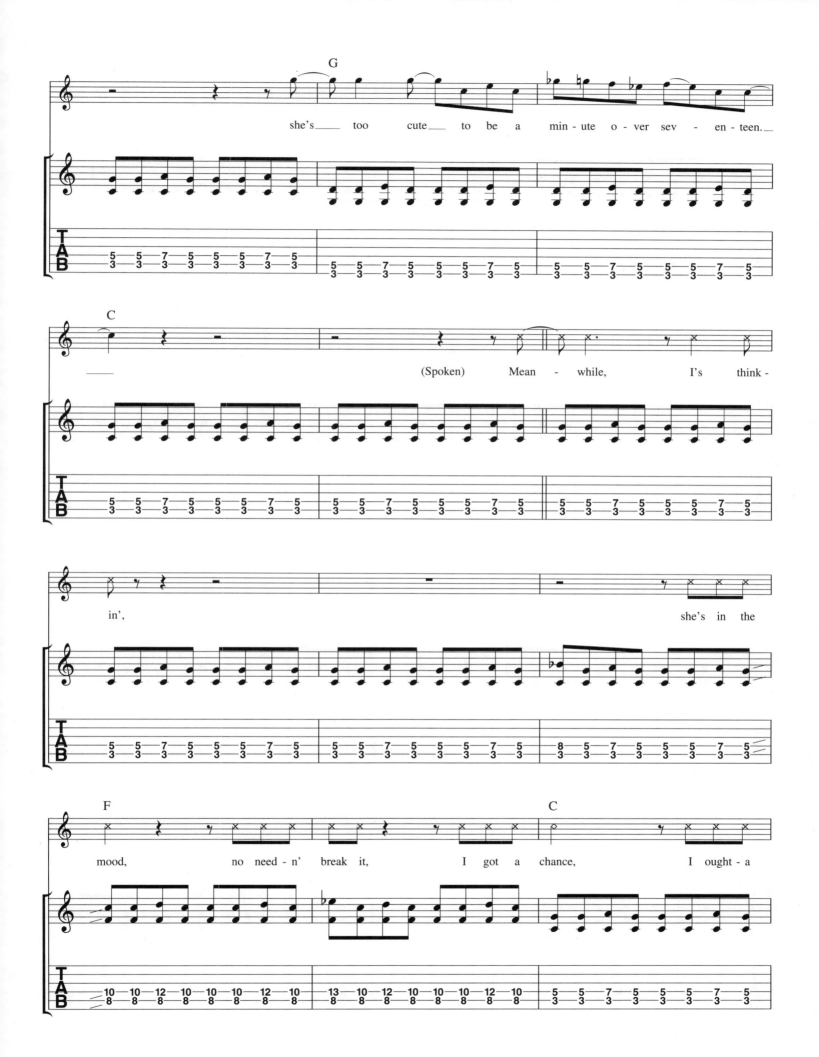

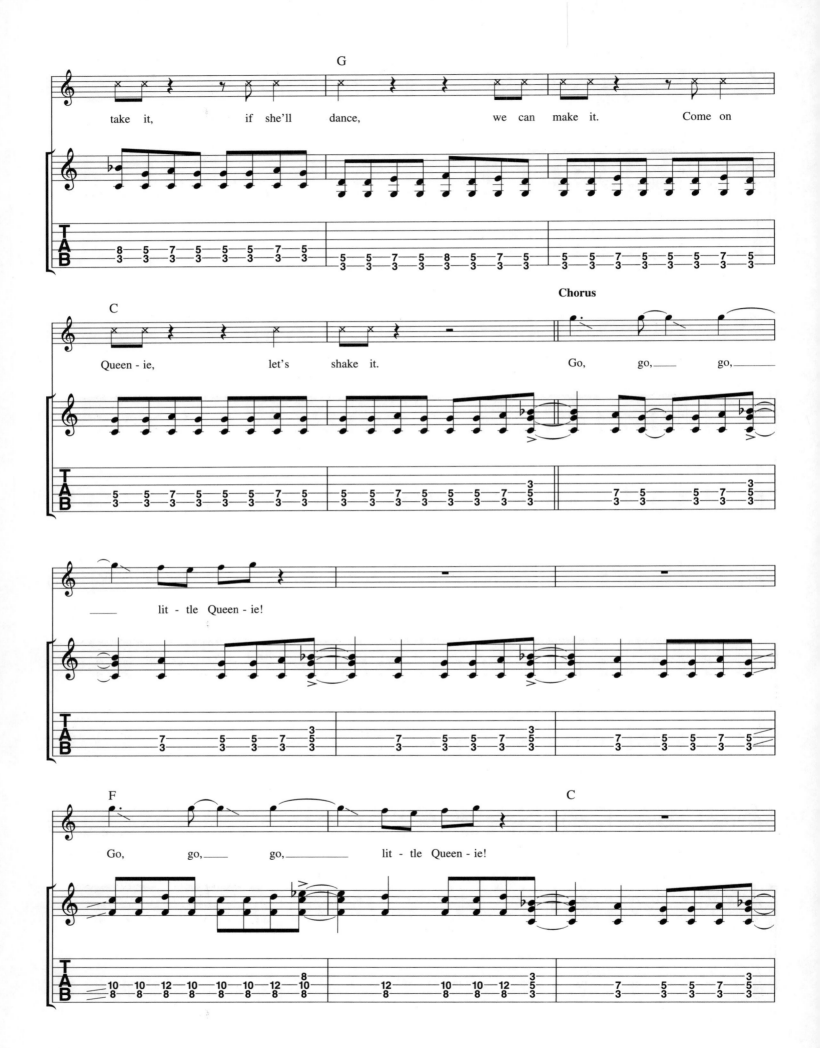

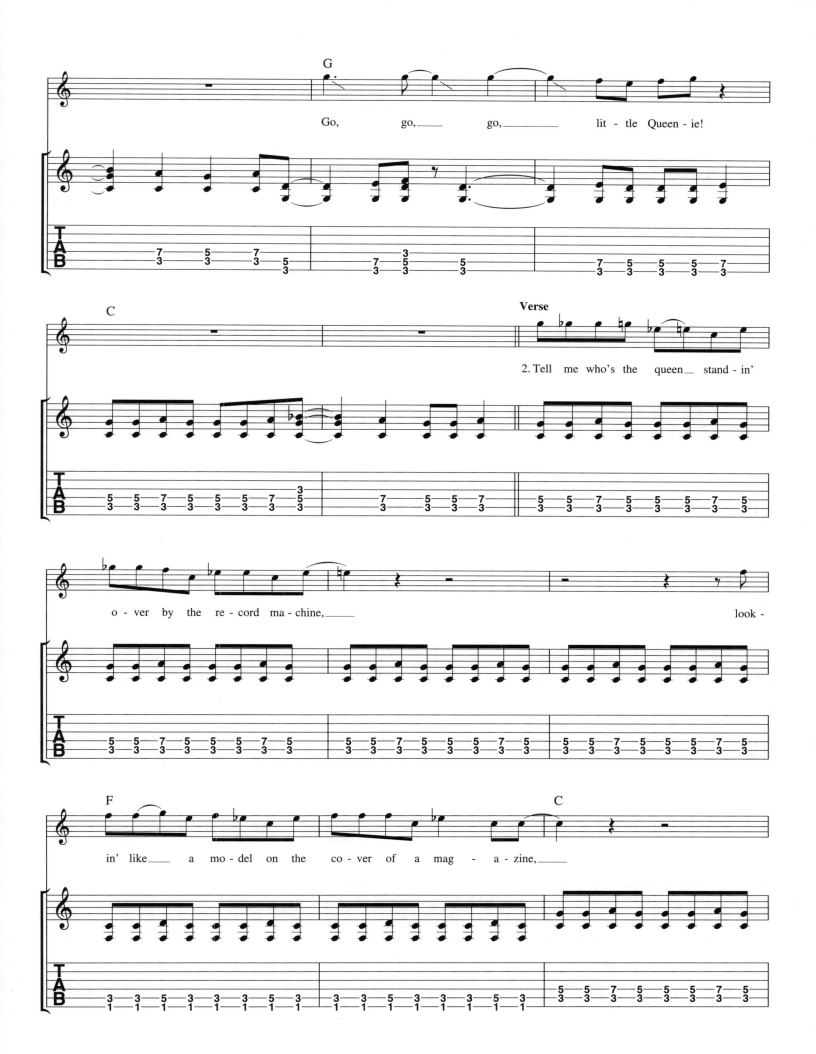

Go, go,___ go,_____ lit - tle Queen - ie!

2. Tell me who's the queen___ stand - in'

o - ver by the re - cord ma - chine,_____ look -

in' like___ a mo - del on the co - ver of a mag - a - zine,_____

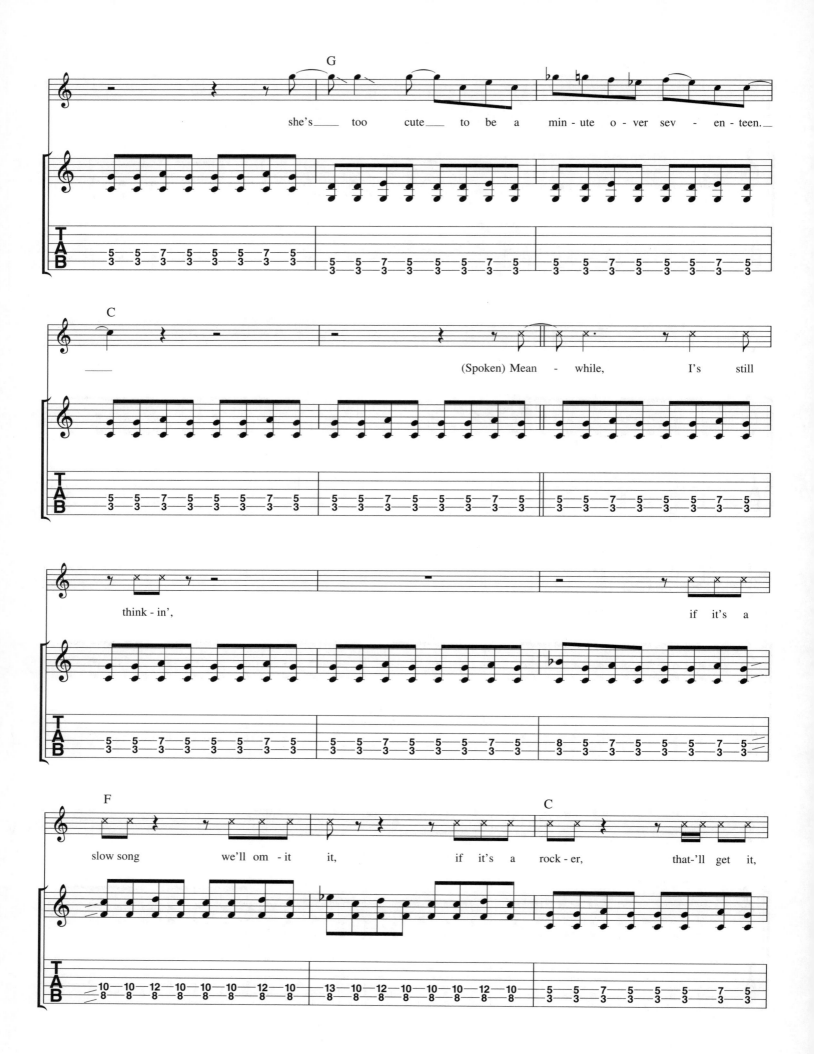

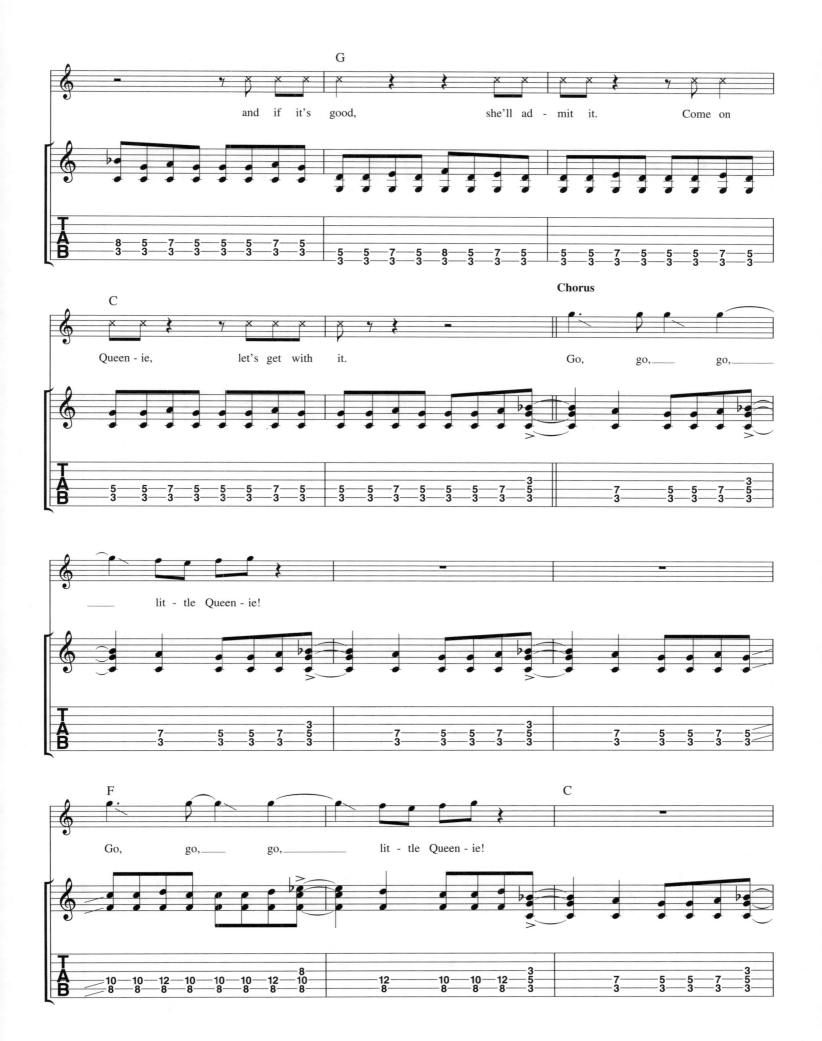

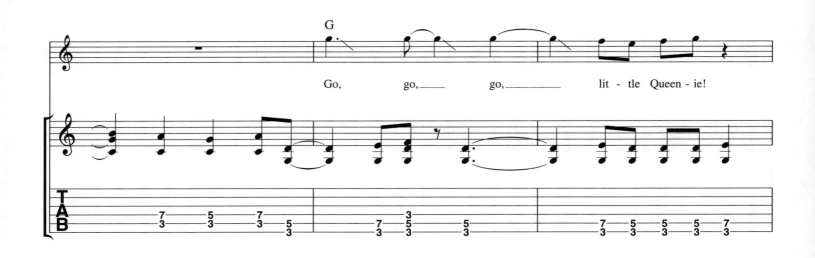

Go,   go,_____   go,_____   lit - tle Queen - ie!

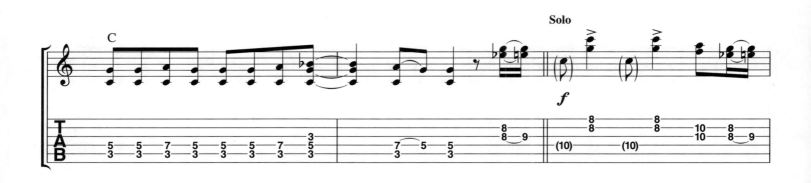

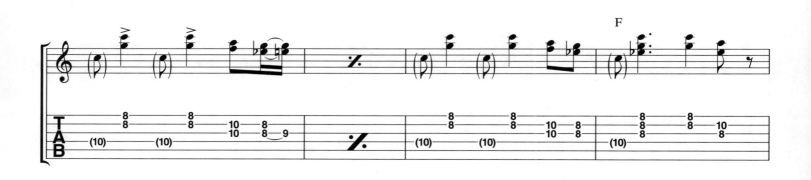

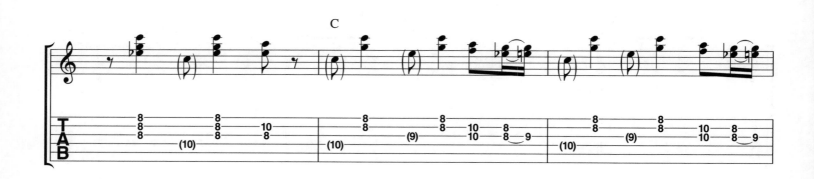

* (The bend from E♭ to E♮ is slightly flat)

Repeat to fade

no particular place to go

Words & Music by Chuck Berry

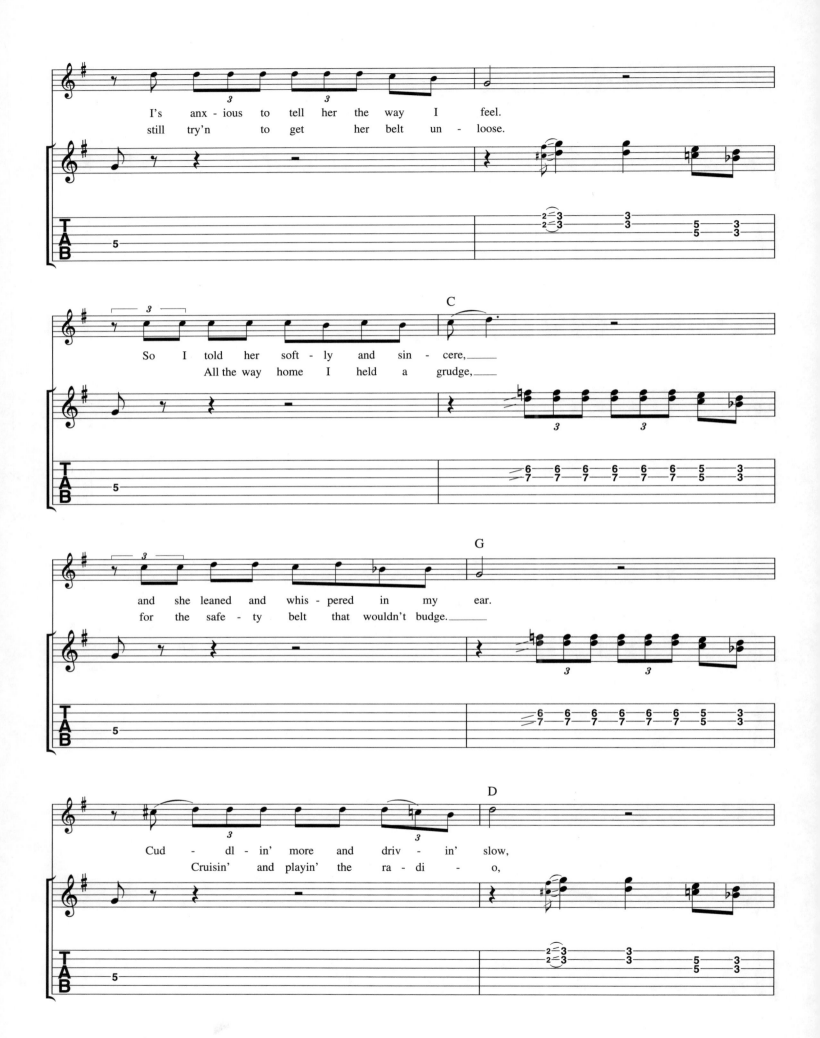

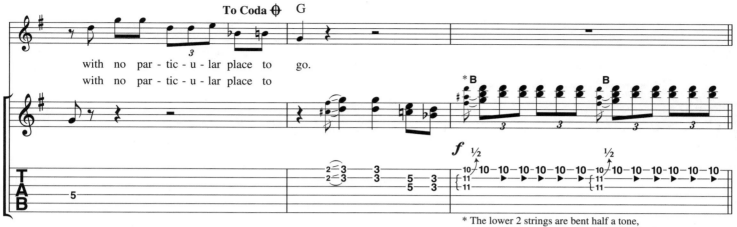

with no par-tic-u-lar place to go.
with no par-tic-u-lar place to

*B   B

* The lower 2 strings are bent half a tone,
then the 2nd string is held and restruck as indicated

Solo

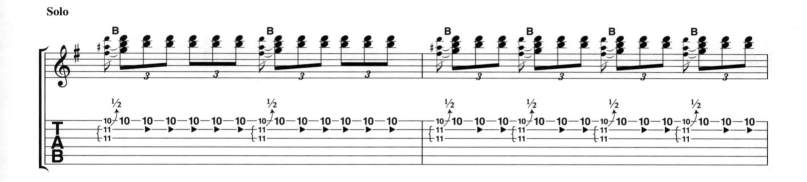

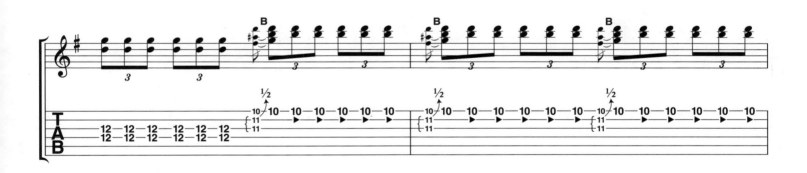

C

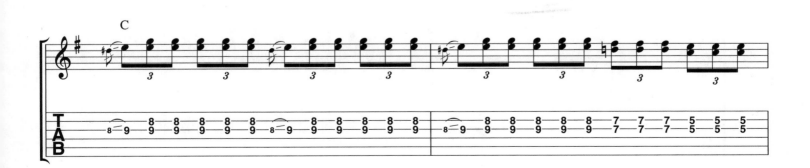

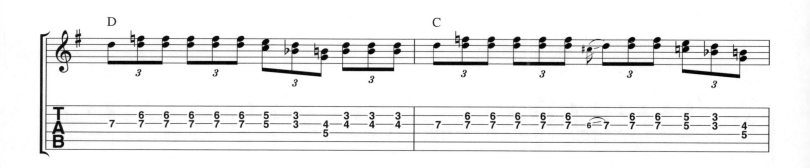

D. ℅ al Coda ✠

3. No par-tic-u-lar place to

* the bend to F is slightly flat

Coda ✠

G

go.

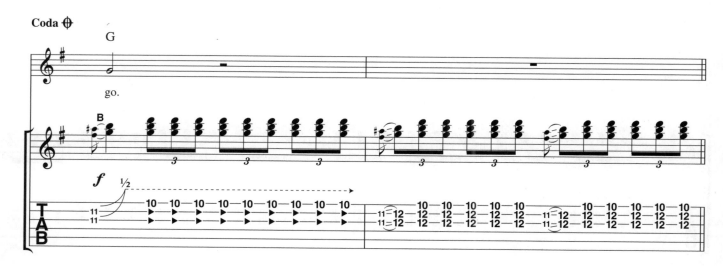

Outro solo

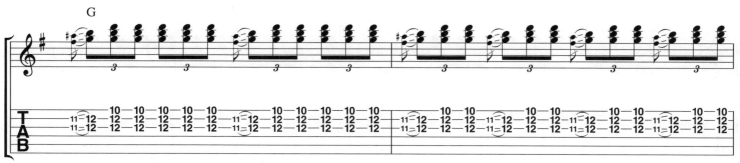

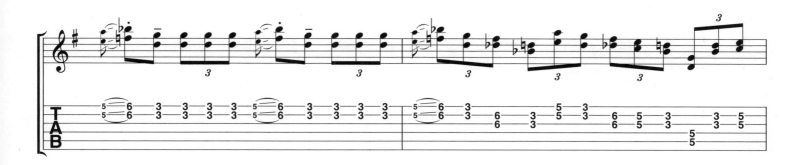

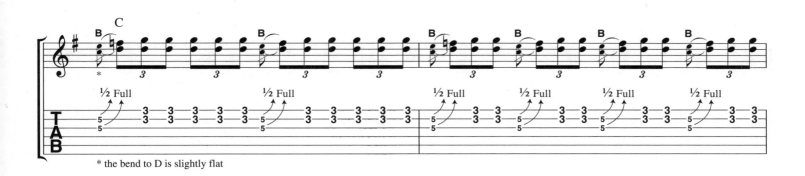

* the bend to D is slightly flat

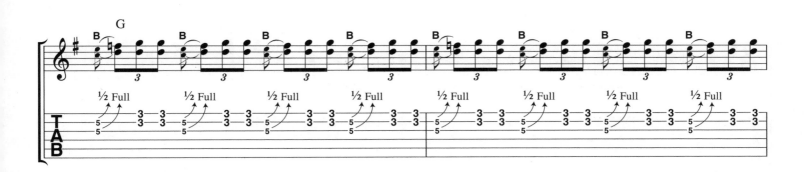

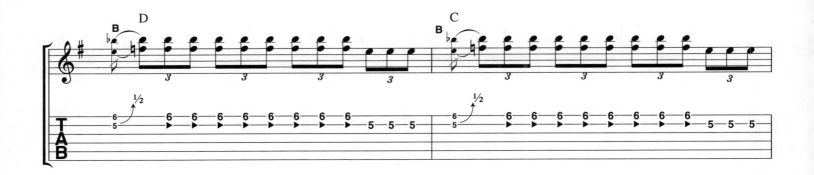

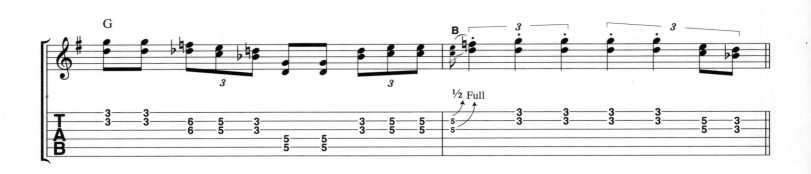

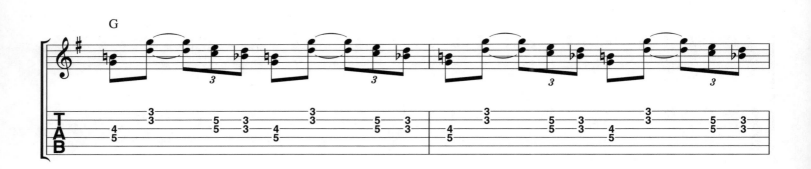

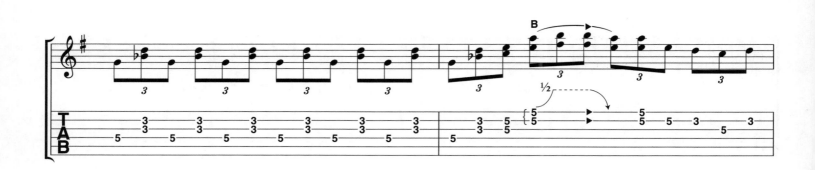

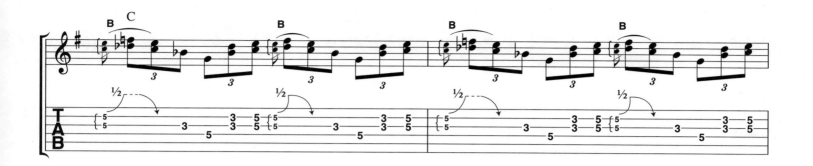

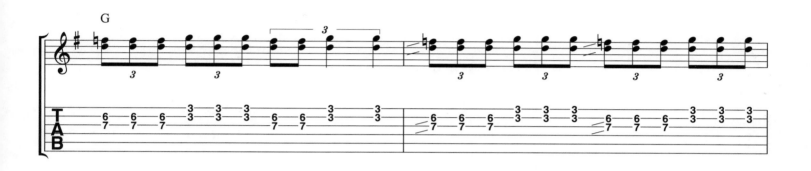

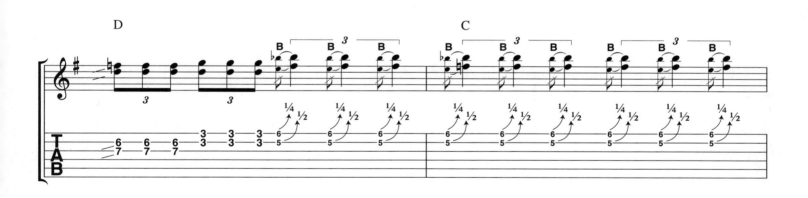

3/00 (36824)

Other great titles in the series include
play guitar with...

the beatles
day tripper
dear prudence
get back
i feel fine
norwegian wood
paperback writer
sgt. pepper's lonely
 hearts club band
yesterday
Order No. NO90665

blur
country house
end of a century
girls and boys
mr. robinson's quango
parklife
stereotypes
the universal
tracy jacks
Order No. AM935320

bon jovi
in and out of love
in these arms
lay your hands on me
livin' on a prayer
never say goodbye
wanted dead or alive
you give love a bad name
Order No. AM92558

eric clapton
bad love
i shot the sheriff
layla
let it grow
sunshine of your love
tears in heaven
white room
wonderful tonight
Order No. AM950862

phil collins
another day in paradise
don't lose my number
i don't wanna know
i wish it would rain down
inside out
one more night
thunder & lightning
Order No. AM928147

the cranberries
dreams
hollywood
how
i can't be with you
ridiculous thoughts
still can't recognise the way i feel
when you're gone
zombie
Order No. AM941699

buddy holly
heartbeat
oh boy
rave on
that'll be the day
words of love
peggy sue
Order No. AM943734

kula shaker
govinda
hey dude
hush
into the deep
knight on the town
smart dogs
tattva
Order No. AM943767

john lennon
cold turkey
come together
happy xmas (war is over)
help!
i want you (she's so heavy)
woman
Order No. AM943756

bob marley
buffalo soldier
could you be loved
exodus
i shot the sheriff
jamming
no woman, no cry
waiting in vain
Order No. AM937739

metallica
ain't my bitch
enter sandman
fade to black
nothing else matters
the unforgiven
welcome home (sanitarium)
Order No. AM92559

alanis morissette
all i really want
hand in my pocket
ironic
mary jane
not the doctor
perfect
you learn
you oughta know
Order No. AM943723

oasis
cigarettes & alcohol
hey now
morning glory
roll with it
she's electric
supersonic
up in the sky
Order No. AM935330

ocean colour scene
the circle
the day we caught the train
fleeting mind
40 past midnight
policemen and pirates
the riverboat song
you've got it bad
Order No. AM943712

elvis presley
all shook up
blue suede shoes
his latest flame (marie's the name)
hound dog
jailhouse rock
king creole
lawdy miss clawdy
my baby left me
Order No. AM937090

pulp
babies
common people
disco 2000
do you remember the first time?
mis-shapes
something changed
sorted for e's & wizz
Order No. AM938124

the rolling stones
brown sugar
get off of my cloud
gimme shelter
honky tonk women
(i can't get no) satisfaction
jumpin' jack flash
19th nervous breakdown
paint it black
Order No. AM90247

sting
an englishman in new york
fields of gold
fragile
if you love somebody set them free
moon over bourbon street
straight to my heart
they dance alone
Order No. AM928092

the stone roses
elephant stone
i am the resurrection
i wanna be adored
made of stone
she bangs the drums
ten storey love song
waterfall
Order No. AM943701

paul weller
the changingman
into tomorrow
out of the sinking
stanley road
sunflower
wild wood
woodcutter's son
you do something to me
Order No. AM937827